THE NATIVITY

THE STORY OF BABY JESUS

THE NATIVITY

THE STORY OF BABY JESUS

May Eliot

Illustrated by Richard Johnson

PICTURE CORGI

Long ago in a little town called Nazareth, lived a young woman called Mary. She was going to be married to Joseph, a carpenter.

One day, when Mary was
alone in her home, an amazing
thing happened.

A beautiful angel shining brightly
appeared and told Mary that he
had some very great news for her.
This was the Angel Gabriel, and
he told Mary that God had chosen
her for a very special task.

She was to have a child, and he would be the son of God.
He would be called Jesus and would be very important for
all of mankind.

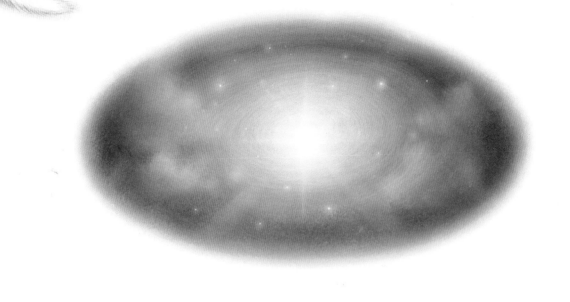

When the Angel Gabriel left, Mary was astonished and amazed.

She told Joseph all that the Angel Gabriel had said, and as time passed she found out that she was indeed to have a baby.

But as the time of the baby's arrival grew nearer, it was
decreed that everyone must go and put their name on a register.
Mary and Joseph would have to travel to Bethlehem.

The journey was long and tiring. Mary and Joseph travelled by donkey, along hot and dusty roads.

Finally they arrived at Bethlehem, but, because of King Herod's decree, it was very busy.

Mary and Joseph needed to find a room for the night, so Joseph knocked at the door of an inn, but he was told that there was no room for him and Mary.

Joseph tried again, and again, but to no avail.
All the inns were full and they were turned away.

It was dark and growing cold and Mary felt sure it wouldn't be long before the baby would be born.

Joseph tried one final inn, and though it was full,
the kindly innkeeper took pity on Mary and Joseph.

He told them that they could sleep in his stable.

Mary and Joseph were very grateful.
They led their donkey into the warm
stable and made a bed in the straw,
amongst the cows and the horses and
the other animals.

Mary knew that her special baby
would soon be born...

And then the baby Jesus came, there in the stable, surrounded by the peaceful watching animals.

Mary wrapped him up to keep him warm and placed
him in a manger, where the hay was kept, for a bed.

Up in the hills some shepherds were watching
their flock by night when they were blinded
by a bright light.

It was an angel and he brought them great news.
He told them that they must go to Bethlehem, where
a very special baby had been born. So they set off
straight away, following a bright star in the sky.

Meanwhile in the East, three wise men also saw this bright new star in the sky.

They knew that a very special baby had been
born and they, too, set off following the star.

It was very peaceful in the stable in Bethlehem. Just then, the door creaked open. The baby's visitors had arrived.

The three shepherds came in, telling Mary and Joseph that they had travelled a long way to see the special baby.

They had brought Jesus a gift of a baby lamb.

And then more visitors arrived. It was the three wise men, bearing beautiful and expensive gifts for the baby Jesus.

One brought gold, one brought myrrh, and one brought
frankincense. They explained that they, too, had followed
the bright star in the sky to come to see the special baby.

The three wise men lay down their gifts
where the baby Jesus lay, in his manger.

The shepherds and the wise men gazed upon his face, and knew - as the angel had foretold - that this baby would be very important for all of mankind.

As the stars twinkled and
the angels sang, Mary, Joseph,
the shepherds, the three wise
men and all the animals gathered
round the baby Jesus together,
for they knew this had been
a very special day.

THE NATIVITY
A PICTURE CORGI BOOK 978 0 552 57470 9
Published in Great Britain by Picture Corgi,
an imprint of Random House Children's Publishers UK
A Random House Group Company
This edition published 2013

3 5 7 9 10 8 6 4 2

Picture Corgi Books are published by Random House Children's Publishers UK,
61–63 Uxbridge Road, London W5 5SA
www.randomhousechildrens.co.uk
www.randomhouse.co.uk
Addresses for companies within The Random House Group Limited can be found at:
www.randomhouse.co.uk/offices.htm

THE RANDOM HOUSE GROUP Limited Reg. No. 954009
A CIP catalogue record for this book is available from the British Library.
Printed in China